RUSLAN RUSSIAN ALPHABET

An introduction to the Cyrillic alphabet fo
and for travellers to Russia and Ukraine
John Langran

C000203069

Ruslan Limited
www.ruslan.co.uk

RUSLAN RUSSIAN ALPHABET STARTER

An introduction to the Cyrillic alphabet for learners of Russian
and for travellers to Russia and Ukraine

John Langran

First edition 2014

© **2014 Ruslan**

ISBN 9781899785919

Design and typesetting by Ruslan Limited

Published by Ruslan Limited

UK Book Trade distribution by Bay Foreign Language Books Limited

Acknowledgements

Thank you to TCBC School Tours for their original idea and imput. Photos are mainly by John
Langran. Thanks for additional photos to Dan Hornby, Håkan Olson, Alexandra Menshikova, Andrey
Podkorytov, Heather Richards, Samara City Council, Gilles Siche, Stepan Kadashnikov, TopFoto
(agents for Ria Novosti) and to Andrew Whitley at Bread Matters.

Introduction

This booklet will help travellers to Russia and Ukraine and learners of Russian to make a start with the Cyrillic alphabet and at the same time meet a wide range of cultural, historical and practical references as a general introduction to the Russian language and to Russia itself.

You can write in the pronunciation in English letters to help you remember the Russian sounds. You can do this in pencil first and then check with a teacher or listen to the recordings before you write in a final version.

Recordings, transliterations of the sounds of the words and other notes and links are on the Ruslan website at www.ruslan.co.uk/alphabetstarter.htm

Football vocabulary has been included for visitors to the Football World Cup in June and July 2018.

I would be grateful to receive ideas and suggestions, as well as more photos from travellers to Russia and Ukraine to illustrate the words in this book and other useful Russian words. Please see the web page.

John Langran
January 2014

Contents

My tour - Мой тур

Fill this in in Russian during your trip!

Имя (your first name)
_____

Фами́лия (your family name)
_____

Аэропо́рт/ы (airport/s used)
_____

Вокза́л/ы (station/s used)
_____

Города́ (cities visited)
_____

Гости́ница/ы (hotel/s)
_____

Люби́мые места́ (favourite places)
_____

_____

_____

Лю́ди (people - names of people you have met)

_____

_____

_____

The Russian alphabet has 33 characters.

There are
20 consonants,
10 vowels,
1 semi vowel or dipthong
and 2 phonetic signs.

А а	Л л	Ч ч
Б б	М м	Ш ш
В в	Н н	Щ щ
Г г	О о	Ъ ъ
Д д	П п	Ы ы
Е е	Р р	Ь ь
Ё ё	С с	Э э
Ж ж	Т т	Ю ю
З з	У у	Я я
И и	Ф ф	
Й й	Х х	
К к	Ц ц	

Six letters are very similar in Russian and English.

а   like "a" in "cat"

е   sounds like "ye" when stressed, or like "e" in "bet"

К   "k" in "kit"

М   "m" in "man"

О   sounds like "o" but more like "a" when unstressed

Т   "t" in "top"

 Use the recordings for the exact pronunciation:
www.ruslan.co.uk/alphabetstarter.htm.

Words with letters you have met so far:

	pronounced (approx.)	meaning
áTOM	átom	atom
TéMA	tyéma	theme
MáMA	máma	mother, mum
KOMéTA	komyéta	comet
KOT	kot	cat

The acute accent ´ is used to show vowels which are stressed. Stress is random in Russian and has to be learned for each new word you meet.

Two letters are similar in Russian and English, but not completely.

C   an "s" sound, like the "c" in "ice"

3   a "z" sound, and the letter looks like our handwritten "z".

Five "false friends" look like English letters but are different.

B   "v" in "van"

p   a rolled "r"

H   "n" in "not"

y   like "oo" in "boot" but with a slight "u"

X   "ch" in the Scottish "loch"

Words with letters you have met so far:

	pronounced (approx.)	meaning
сáуна	sáoona	sauna
кóсмос	kósmos	space
зоопáрк	zaopárk	zoo
вáза	váza	vase
самовáр	samovár	samovar
рот	rot	mouth
ракéта	rakyéta	rocket
нет	nyet	no
нос	nos	nose
Урá!	Urá!	Hurrah!
тур	toor	tour
хор	khor	choir

Самовáр - A samovar.
For making tea.

You may perhaps recognise six letters from Greek or from formulae in maths.

б   "b" in "bed"

Г   a hard "g" as in "get"

Д   "d" in "dot"

Л   "l" in "lad"

П   "p" in "pot"

ф   "f" in "fat"

Words with letters you have met so far:

	pronounced (approx.)	meaning
бана́н	banán	banana
банк	bank	bank
газ	gaz	gas
грамм	gramm	gram
да	da	yes
до́ктор	dóktor	doctor
ла́мпа	lámpa	lamp
бале́т	balyét	ballet
пробле́ма	problyéma	problem
Пра́вда	Právda	Pravda (newspaper)
факт	fakt	fact
футбо́л	footból	football

Бале́т «Лебеди́ное о́зеро»
The ballet "Swan Lake".

The remaining letters are unlike English letters. There are six vowels

Ё   "yo" (always stressed)

И   "ee" in "meet"

Ы   like the "i" in "bit" but harder

Э   like the hard "e" in "bet"

Ю   like the soft "u" in "use"

Я   like the "ya" in "yak"

and one "semi-vowel".

Й   a dipthong like the "y" in "boy"

Words with letters you have met so far:

	pronounced (approx.)	meaning
ёлка	yólka	fir tree
репортёр	reportyór	reporter
идиóт	idiót	idiot
рáдио	rádio	radio
ви́за	víza	visa
кинó	kinóh	cinema
Крым	Krim	Crimea
эффéкт	effékt	effect
юри́ст	yuríst	lawyer
я́блоко	yábloko	apple
йóгурт	yógoort	yoghurt
май	mai	May

Крым - The Crimea.

There are five strange consonants

Ж - "s" in "pleasure"

Ц - "ts"

Ч - "ch"

Ш - "sh"

Щ - a longer "sh" or "sch"

and there are two phonetic signs.

ь - a soft sign makes the previous consonant softer

ъ - a hard sign separates a consonant from a soft vowel

Words with letters you have met so far:

	pronounced (approx.)	meaning
журна́л	zhoornál	journal
царь	tsar	tsar
цеме́нт	tsemént	cement
чай	chay	tea
чемпио́н	chempión	champion
шокола́д	shokolád	chocolate
щи	schi	cabbage soup
борщ	borsch	beetroot soup
Кремль	Kreml'	the Kremlin
объе́кт	ob'ékt	object

Моско́вский Кремль - The Moscow Kremlin.

The alphabet printed and written

Write in the sounds when you have learned them.

Printed	Written	Sound		Printed	Written	Sound		Printed	Written	Sound
А а	$\mathscr{A}$ a	a		К к	$\mathscr{K}$ $к$	k		Х х	$\mathscr{X}$ x	ch
Б б	$\mathscr{B}$ $б$	b		Л л	$\mathscr{L}$ $л$	l		Ц ц	$\mathscr{U}$ $ц$	ts
В в	$\mathscr{B}$ $в$	v		М м	$\mathscr{M}$ $м$	m		Ч ч	$\mathscr{Ч}$ $ч$	ch
Г г	$\mathscr{G}$ $г$	g		Н н	$\mathscr{H}$ $н$	n		Ш ш	$\mathscr{Ш}$ $ш$	sh
Д д	$\mathscr{D}$ g/д	d		О о	$\mathscr{O}$ o	o		Щ щ	$\mathscr{Щ}$ $щ$	sch
Е е	$\mathscr{E}$ $е$	e		П п	$\mathscr{П}$ $п$	p		ъ	$ъ$	
Ё ё	$\ddot{\mathscr{E}}$ $ё$	yo		Р р	$\mathscr{P}$ $р$	r		Ы ы	$ы$ $ы$	i
Ж ж	$\mathscr{Ж}$ $ж$	s		С с	$\mathscr{C}$ $с$	s		ь	$ь$	
З з	$\mathscr{Z}$ $з$	z		Т т	$\mathscr{T}$ m/т	t		Э э	$\mathscr{Э}$ $э$	e
И и	$\mathscr{U}$ $и$	ee		У у	$\mathscr{У}$ $у$	oo		Ю ю	$\mathscr{Ю}$ $ю$	u
Й й	$\mathscr{Й}$ $й$	y		Ф ф	$\mathscr{F}$ $ф$	f		Я я	$\mathscr{Я}$ $я$	ya

Find your way!

Guess some street signs:

(1)

(2)

(3)

Supermarket

(4)

(5)

toilet

(6)

stop

(7)

cafe

(8)

ФОТО

photos

Which is which?
Wine
Supermarket
Museum
Cash Machine
Café
Photos
Stop
Toilet

Which city is which?

(1)

Новосибирск

(2)

Санкт-Петербург

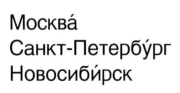

Москва́
Санкт-Петербу́рг
Новосиби́рск

(3)

Москва́

Росси́я от А до Я
Russia from A to Ya

The next pages give you an A to Z of cultural, historical and other references to help you start to read the Cyrillic script. These are interactive pages. You can write in the sounds of the words in the underlined gaps and then check them on the Ruslan website.

Вперёд!

Vperyod!

Onwards!

Абракада́бра - _____ *

This is used for "gobbledegook". Something you can't understand. You get абракада́бра when you try to type in Russian with the wrong font, for example:
Àáðàêàä,áðà

* Write in the sound of the word in English letters. Sometimes it will be similar to the English word, sometimes a little different, sometimes completely different. Check your answers at www.ruslan.co.uk/alphabetstarter.htm

Авро́ра - _____

The battle cruiser "Aurora" fired the first shots in the Russian Revolution of 1917. It is now moored on the river Neva in Saint Petersburg.

Кре́йсер «Авро́ра»

Алфави́т - _____

The Cyrillic alphabet has evolved from the "Glagolithic" alphabet created by Greek holy men Cyril and Methodius in the 9th century AD. It is used in Russia, Ukraine, Belarus, Bulgaria and Serbia.

Recordings are at www.ruslan.co.uk/alphabetstarter.htm

Ruslan Russian Alphabet Starter

Арба́т - _____

A famous street in central Moscow, now pedestrianised. An important tourist attraction with street sellers, souvenir shops and restaurants.

У́лица «Арба́т»

Авто́бус - _____

The bus is a common and cheap means of transport. Buy your ticket - биле́т _____ from a кио́ск _____ before you get on.

Атле́тика - _____

This is "Athletics". Very popular in Russia in the summer.

A a

Байка́л - _____

Very large lake in central Siberia, 636 kilometres long with a width from 25 to 80 kilometres and a depth of 1637 metres at its deepest point. The lake is estimated to contain 20% of the world's freshwater reserves.

Большо́й теа́тр - _____

Iconic theatre in central Moscow, famous for its ballet and opera performances.

Балала́йка - _____

Traditional Russian three-stringed instrument.

Ruslan Russian Alphabet Starter

Ба́ня - _____

This is a Russian public wash house with steam baths like a sauna.

Борщ - _____

This is beetroot soup, a popular dish in Russia and Ukraine. There is a saying that there are as many recipes for борщ as there are Russian housewives.

Михаи́л Булга́ков -

_____

Popular Russian writer and playwright during the Soviet period.

A famous book by Михаи́л Булга́ков – «Ма́стер и Маргари́та».

_____

_____

ВВЦ - _____

"The All Russian Exhibition Centre". In Soviet times this was
ВДНХ (_____) - "The Exhibition of the Achievements
of the People's Economy". ВВЦ is in the north of Moscow and
well worth a visit. The metro station you should use is still
called ВДНХ.

Владивосто́к - _____

A city on the Russian eastern coast. The name literally means
"Commander of the East".

Во́дка - _____

It is usual to drink only when someone in the group
proposes a toast, especially in a formal situation.
Whose is the brand of vodka in the picture?
«Пути́нка» _____

Во́лга - _____

This is the longest river in Europe, 6058 miles long.
The source is north of Moscow and the river flows
through Central Russia to the Caspian Sea.

Towns on this river:

_____

_____

_____

_____

_____

_____

_____

Яросла́вль

Ни́жний Но́вгород

Каза́нь

МОСКВА́

Сама́ра

Сара́тов

Волгогра́д

А́страхань

Всё - _____

This useful little word means "everything".

"Is that all?"   – Это всё?   – _____

"Yes, that's all".   – Да, всё.   – _____

В в

Михаи́л Горбачёв - _____

General Secretary of the Communist Party of the Soviet Union (1985-91) and the only President of the Soviet Union (1990-91). Introduced перестро́йка _____ , the restructuring of the economic and political system, and гла́сность _____ , increased openness and freedom of opinion. Presided over the breakup of the USSR in 1991.

ГУМ - _____

This is the Main Universal Shop - Гла́вный Универса́льный Магази́н -

_____,

the largest and most famous shop in central Moscow. If you get lost, then meet by the fountain - фонта́н - _____.

Ю́рий Гага́рин - _____

The first man in space, orbiting the earth in the спу́тник _____
«Восто́к 1» - _____ on 12th April 1961.

Газпро́м - _____

The largest gas company in the world and the largest company in Russia.

Г г

Words and music are at
www.ruslan.co.uk/alphabetstarter.htm

Национа́льный гимн -

_____

The national anthem.

Гри́вна - _____

The Ukrainian unit of currency.

Где - _____

This means "where".

"Where is my passport?"	– Где мой па́спорт?	– _____
"There it is!"	– Вот он!	– _____
"Thank you"	– Спаси́бо.	– _____

Ду́ма - _____

The lower house of the Russian parliament.

Декабри́сты - _____

A group of Russian army officers who rebelled against Tsar Nicholas I in 1825. They were defeated by the Tsar's armed forces, five were executed and many exiled to Siberia.

«Декабри́сты». Painting by K.I.Kolman.

Дом - _____

This can mean home or a house or a large block of flats.

Фёдор Достое́вский - _____

Great Russian 19th century philosophical novelist. His works include «Преступле́ние и Наказа́ние» - "Crime and Punishment", «Бра́тья Карама́зовы» - "The Brothers Karamazov" - and «Идио́т» - _____.

Домоде́дово - _____

Large international airport to the south of Moscow.

До свида́ния - _____

This is "Goodbye". Literally the same as the French "Au revoir".

Да́ча - _____

A small house in the country, often built from wood. Used by families for weekends in the summer and for growing fruit and vegetables.

Да́ча

Достопримеча́тельности - _____

The sights. Literally "things worth noting". See pages 70-73.

Да - ____

Yes.

Бори́с Е́льцин -

First president of Russia (1991-99) and the first freely elected leader of the country. Responsible for initiating the transformation of the Russian economy after the fall of the USSR.

Бори́с Никола́евич Е́льцин

Енисе́й - _____

River in Siberia 2566 miles long.

Евге́ний Евтуше́нко - _____

Siberian born poet of the Soviet era, now living in the USA.

Ёлка - _____

This is a fir tree, but if you are invited to a ёлка you can expect a New Year party.

We invite you to the New Year party!

Ёлки-па́лки! - _____

A common expression of exasperation or surprise.

Ма́ршал Жу́ков - _____

Leader of the Soviet armies in the Great Fatherland War 1941-1945.
His monument is in the centre of Moscow in Manezhnaya Square -
Мане́жная пло́щадь.

Же́нский день - _____

This is Women's Day, March 8th, a State holiday in Russia.
Men give presents to female relatives, colleagues and friends.

Жигули́ - _____

Popular name of the Russian car that is known
in the West as a «Ла́да» _____.

ЗИЛ - _____

Large luxury car from the Soviet period, used by top politicians and party officials. The Russian equivalent of the Rolls Royce.

Ж ж and З з

Здрáвствуйте! - _____

This is "Hello!". It is difficult to pronounce. If you have a standard English accent then think of a donkey and try saying "Does your ass fit you?", slurring the words slightly. The result can be very close to «Здрáвствуйте!».

Закры́то - _____

This means "closed".

И́мя - _____

This means a first name. Here are some common male and female first names:

Алекса́ндр	_____	Алекса́ндра	_____
Андре́й	_____	А́нна	_____
Бори́с	_____	Мари́я	_____
Влади́мир	_____	Ната́лья	_____
Ива́н	_____	Ни́на	_____
Михаи́л	_____	О́льга	_____
Никола́й	_____	Татья́на	_____
Серге́й	_____	Светла́на	_____

Интури́ст - _____

The Russian State tourism organisation.

Икра́ - _____

Caviar, black or red. Roe of sturgeon, beluga or salmon.

Чёрная и кра́сная икра́ -
Black and red caviar.

Извини́те! - _____

"Excuse me!". Use this to attract somene's attention.

Йо́гурт - _____

This is not traditionally Russian. Кефи́р _____ is more widely used.
See page 39.

Трамва́й - _____

Cheap means of transport in cities.

Киóск - _____

Here you can buy newspapers, bus and tram tickets, etc.
The picture is of a traditional киоск in Томск – _____.

Комáр - _____

A mosquito. Present in large numbers in some rural areas
in June and July.

Кремль - _____

There is a kremlin not only in Moscow but also in the centre of several old Russian cities,
for example Нóвгород _____ and Казáнь _____.
The word кремль means "fortress".

Кúев - _____

Capital of Ukraine and the spiritual Christian Orthodox centre of old Russia.

Ка́ша - _____

A sort of porridge, often made from buckwheat, a very traditional
Russian side dish for breakfast, lunch or the evening meal.

К к

Кефи́р - _____

Rather like йо́гурт _____ but a
runnier consistency.

Коне́чно - _____

"Of course". A useful word, especially when you
are bored with saying "да". «Коне́чно» is actually
pronounced «коне́шно». _____.

Квас - _____

A pleasant, very slightly alcoholic drink made from fermented
rye bread. It is often sold in the street.

Исáак Левитáн - _____

Famous landscape painter of the late 19th century, born in Lithuania.

Исáак Левитáн - «Берёзовая рóща» - The birch grove.

Владúмир Ильúч Лéнин -

Russian communist revolutionary and politician who masterminded the October Revolution in 1917 and who led the USSR until his death in 1924.

Ле́на - _____

This river flows from near Lake Baikal to the Laptev Sea in the far north. 2800 miles long, it is the tenth longest river in the world.

Л л

Лубя́нка - _____

This building in central Moscow was once a political prison and headquarters of the КГБ - _____. Today it is used by the ФСБ - _____ (Federal Security Service).

Ла́йка - _____

The first dog in Space.

Ла́дно! - _____

Useful little word meaning "OK" or "alright".

Мать - _____

This means "mother". The image of "Mother Russia" was very strongly emphasised during the Great Fatherland War, 1941-1945.
Family members:

mother	мать	_____
father	отéц	_____
daughter	дочь	_____
son	сын	_____
sister	сестрá	_____
brother	брат	_____
grandfather	дéдушка	_____
grandmother	бáбушка	_____

Your mother country is calling!

Маршрýтка - _____

A minibus taxi which follows a set route like a bus.

Матрёшка - _____

Traditional Russian set of nested dolls.

Матрёшки - Sets of dolls.

Ruslan Russian Alphabet Starter

Москва́ - _____

Capital city of the Russian Federation and the city with the highest population in Europe (11.5 million according to the 2010 census). Moscow was founded in 1147.

Метро́ - _____

Underground railway system. Metro stations in Moscow are renowned for their elaborate architecture.

Ме́дный вса́дник - _____

This is the Bronze Horseman, a monument to Peter the Great in Saint Petersburg. It is also the title of an epic poem by Aleksander Pushkin, one of the most significant works in Russian literature.

Мо́жно? - _____

Use this for "May I ...?". Use it with a verb infinitive (page 69) to ask whether you may do something, or you can just say «Мо́жно?» and hope that what you want is understood!

"May I have a look?   – Мо́жно посмотре́ть?   – _____
"No!"   – Нет!   – _____

М м

Новосиби́рск - _____

Largest city in Siberia.

Some cities in Siberia and the Far East:

_____

_____

_____

_____

_____

_____

_____

Магада́н

Верхоя́нск

Томск

Яку́тск

Новосиби́рск

Хаба́ровск

Ирку́тск

Владивосто́к

Но́вый год - _____

The New Year. Russia has a long winter holiday, with Christmas -
Рождество́ _____ celebrated on January 7th.

Нева́ - _____

River which passes through north-western Russia and
flows into the Baltic Sea at Saint Petersburg.

The embankment of the river Neva in Saint
Petersburg in the 18th century.

Нет - _____
"No".

Нельзя́ - _____

The opposite of «можно» (page 43). This means that you can't do something.

Одéсса - _____

Large port in Ukraine on the Black Sea - Чёрное мóре
_____. Famous for the dramatic
scenes on the Odessa steps in the Eisenstein film
"Battleship Potyomkin".

Олимпи́йские и́гры -

_____

The Olympic Games were held in Moscow in 1980. The Winter
Olympics are to be held in Sochi in 2014.

Остáнкино - _____

Moscow suburb, location of the Moscow television tower with breathtaking views and a
revolving restaurant "Seventh Heaven" - «Седьмóе Нéбо» - _____.

О́тчество - _____

O o

This is the Russian middle name, derived from the name of the father.
Here are some examples. You can work out the father's name.

Male		Female	
Андре́евич	_____	Андре́евна	_____
Бори́сович	_____	Бори́совна	_____
Миха́йлович	_____	Миха́йловна	_____

In formal situations and in formal correspondance Russians use the first name (page 36) and the father's name together, for example President Putin would be addressed as
Влади́мир Влади́мирович - _____.

Обме́н валю́ты - _____

Currency exchange. A common notice in the street in large cities.

Откры́то - _____

This means "open".

Алекса́ндр Серге́евич Пу́шкин -

Poet and writer 1799-1837. Renowned as Russia's greatest literary figure.

Пётр Пе́рвый - _____

Peter the First, or Peter the Great, Tsar of Russia 1682 - 1725,
founder of Saint Petersburg and a great westerniser.

Влади́мир Пу́тин - _____

President of Russia 2000 - 2008 and from May 2012.

Пу́лково - _____

International airport in Saint Petersburg.

Пельме́ни - _____

Small stuffed dumplings from Siberia.

Пра́вда - _____

This means "the truth". It is the name of
the main newspaper from the Soviet period.

Пожа́луйста! - _____

This means "Please":
"Tell me please, where is the metro?" – Скажи́те, пожа́луйста, где метро́?
– _____

Or you can use it like this:
"Thank you".   – Спаси́бо.   – _____
"You're welcome". – Пожа́луйста.   – _____

Приве́т! - _____

This means "Hi!". Only use it informally.

Ры́ба - _____

Fish. Fishing is a popular Russian pastime. Fishing trips can take several days.

Распу́тин - _____

Holy man who was a healer for Aleksey the sick son of Tsar Nicholas II and as a result became a Court favourite. In 1916 he was murdered by group of noblemen because of his supposed harmful influence.

Степа́н Ра́зин - _____

Leader of a major Cossack and peasant rebellion in Southern Russian in 1670.

Револю́ция - _____

This means "revolution". In the Russian Revolution of 1917 the Communist Bolsheviks overthrew the Tsarist regime.

Р р

Рубль - _____

The Russian unit of currency.

500 roubles - пятьсо́т рубле́й
_____

Рестора́н - _____

This means "restaurant".

Санкт-Петербу́рг - _____

Founded in 1703 by Peter the Great as a window into Europe, this was Russia's capital from the early 18th century until 1918. It is the second largest city in Russia with a population of nearly five million (2010). Many Russians call the city just «Пи́тер» - _____.

Ио́сиф Ста́лин - _____

Leader of the Soviet Union following Lenin's death in 1924. He established the Soviet Union as a world power and secured victory over the Nazis in the Second World War. A ruthless dictator whose purges resulted in millions of deaths.

Смета́на - _____

Sour cream, a popular ingredient in many Russian sweet and savoury dishes.

Сапса́н - _____

Express train between Moscow and Saint Petersburg, reducing the journey to three hours and forty minutes.

Сиби́рь - _____

A vast area to the east of the Ural mountains, rich in mineral resources, 77% of the area of the Russian Federation.

За́падная Сиби́рь - Western Siberia.

Снег - _____

Snow.

Спаси́бо - _____

"Thank you", literally in old Russian: "May God save you!"

Лев Никола́евич Толсто́й -

_____

Famous Russian 19th century novelist. His most famous works "War and Peace" and "Anna Karenina" are renowned worldwide for their vivid depiction of life and feelings.

Трансси́б - _____

The Trans-Siberian Railway is the longest railway in the world (5772 miles long). It connects Moscow and European Russian with the Russian Far East, Mongolia and China.

Валенти́на Терешко́ва - _____

Soviet cosmonaut. The first woman to fly in space.

Та́нцы - _____

Dances. The Russians have a very strong folk dance tradition.

Третьяко́вская галере́я - _____

An art gallery with a wonderful collection of Russian art. Given to the city of Moscow
by the art collector and merchant Па́вел Третьяко́в - _____.

Ура́л - _____

Mountain range that runs North to South. A boundary between Europe and Asia.

Ю́жный Ура́л - The Southern Urals.

Узбекиста́н - _____

Central Asian state, formally a Republic of the Soviet Union. Russian is still widely used here.

Ура́! - _____

Equivalent of "hooray" or "hurrah".

ФСБ - _____

Russia's main security agency. Successor to
the КГБ - _____.

У у and Ф ф

Фами́лия - _____

This is the family name. Here are some common examples:

Male		Female	
Андре́ев	_____	Андре́ева	_____
Ивано́в	_____	Ивано́ва	_____
Козло́в	_____	Козло́ва	_____
Жуко́вский	_____	Жуко́вская	_____
Ники́тин	_____	Ники́тина	_____
Серге́ев	_____	Серге́ева	_____

Футбо́л - _____

A popular sport in the summer. Because of the vast distances it is not possible to organise
a full national league. See page 87. Футза́л _____ is played indoors in winter.

Хлеб - _____

Russian bread is often of high quality and includes some excellent rye breads.

Бородинский хлеб - Borodinsky bread.

Хоккéй - _____

This is ice hockey, a major national sport.

Храм - _____

A temple or cathedral. The most important Orthodox cathedral in Russia is the Cathedral of Christ the Saviour - Храм Христá Спасúтеля _____ in Moscow.

Хорошó - _____

This means "good" or "fine".

"How are things?"   – Как делá?   – _____
"Fine, thanks".   – Хорошó, спасúбо. – _____

Царь - _____

The Russian monarch, until 1917.

Х х and Ц ц

Це́рковь - _____

The church. The Russian Orthodox Church was persecuted in Soviet times. It is now very strong.

ЦУМ - _____

Central Universal Shop. The Moscow ЦУМ is exceptionally fashionable and expensive.

Ци́фры - _____

Numbers. Write in the sounds of the numbers 0-10

0	ноль	_____			
1	оди́н	_____	6	шесть	_____
2	два	_____	7	семь	_____
3	три	_____	8	во́семь	_____
4	четы́ре	_____	9	де́вять	_____
5	пять	_____	10	де́сять	_____

Антóн Пáвлович Чéхов -

_____

Russian short story writer and playwright (1860-1904).
Which of his plays is in the poster?

_____ .

ПРЕМЬЕРА
А. П. ЧЕХОВ
ДЯДЯ ВАНЯ
Сцены из деревенской жизни в 2 частях

Режиссер-постановщик
Художественный руководитель театра
Римас ТУМИНАС

Чай - _____
Russians drink a lot of tea, either with milk or with a slice of lemon.

Tea with milk.	Чай с молокóм.	_____
Tea with lemon.	Чай с лимóном.	_____

Пётр Ильич Чайко́вский - _____

Composer, 1840-1893. His works include:

ballets	бале́ты	_____
operas	о́перы	_____
symphonies	симфо́нии	_____
concertos	конце́рты	_____

(конце́рт can also mean a concert)

Черепа́ха - _____

A tortoise. Not a very useful word, but we hope you will like it!

Что? - _____

What? A very useful word!

"What is this?".	– Что э́то?.	– _____
"I don't know".	– Я не зна́ю.	– _____

Шампа́нское -

_____

A Russian sparkling white wine.

Шокола́д -

_____

Russian chocolate is excellent. One famous
chocolate factory is "Red October" -
"Кра́сный Октя́брь" - _____.

Шампа́нское «Наде́жда»
"Nadezhda" champagne.

Шокола́д «Алёнка».
"Alyonka" chocolate.

Мари́я Шара́пова - _____

Top Russian tennis player.

Шереме́тьево -

_____

International airport in northern Moscow.

Ш ш and Щ щ

Ша́пка - _____

A traditional Russian fur hat.

Ру́сская ша́пка - A Russian hat.

Щи - _____

Soup made with cabbage.

Щелку́нчик - _____

"The Nutcracker". Popular ballet by Чайко́вский.

Ыгыа́тта - _____

A river in the Far East, notable for the fact that it is one of very few place names beginning with the letter «ы».

Apart from a small number of place names, there are no Russian words that begin with ы.

Крым - _____

The Crimea. A peninsular in the Black Sea, now part of Ukraine.

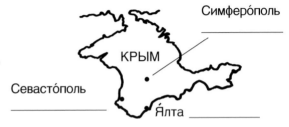

Симферо́поль _____

КРЫМ

Севасто́поль _____

Я́лта _____

Ты and Вы - _____

These are the two Russian words for "you".
Ты is used for friends or relatives in the singular.
Вы is used more formally to show respect, and is used for the plural.

Here are all the personal pronouns:

I	Я ___
you (informal, singular)	ТЫ ___
he or it	ОН ___
she or it	ОНА́ ___
it	ОНО́ ___
we	МЫ ___
you (formal or plural)	ВЫ ___
they	ОНИ́ ___

Мы - _____

The Russian for "we".

Эрмита́ж - _____

Museum in Saint Petersburg on the banks of the river Нева́ _____. It houses about three million items, including the largest collection of paintings in the world.

Ы ы and Э э

Э́то - _____

The word for "this".

"Who is this?"   — Кто э́то?   — _____

"It is Ivan".   — Э́то Ива́н.   — _____

Юг - _____

This means "south". The former Югославия _____
was "The land of the Southern Slavs". Here are the four points of the compass:

Се́вер _____

За́пад

Восто́к

Ю́мор - _____

Humour. Often difficult for learners to understand
because of plays on words.

Юг _____

Я - _____

The word for "I" in Russian. This is only written
as a capital at the beginning of a sentence.

Я́лта - _____

Crimean resort now in Ukraine. Location for the conference between Roosevelt, Churchill and Stalin in 1945.

Я́годы и грибы́ - _____

"Berries and mushrooms". A vital part of Russian country life.

Лев Я́шин - _____

Often considered to be the greatest goalkeeper in the history of football.

Ямщи́к - _____

A coachman on his тро́йка _____ .
This is a traditional Russian folk image.

Подъе́зд - _____

Russian apartment blocks and other large buildings often
have several outside entrances. These are called a подъе́зд
and are numbered.

"Which entrance?" — Како́й подъе́зд? — _____

"The third". — Тре́тий. — _____

The hard sign ъ is not used very often.

Янва́рь - _____

This is January. Many of the months of the year are spelled with soft signs.

Ъ and **Ь**

hard sign and soft sign

Work out the sounds of the months of the year:

янва́рь	_____	ию́ль	_____
февра́ль	_____	а́вгуст	_____
март	_____	сентя́брь	_____
апре́ль	_____	октя́брь	_____
май	_____	ноя́брь	_____
ию́нь	_____	дека́брь	_____

Рабо́тать - _____

This means "to work". Most Russian verb infinitives end in -ть. For example:

"to do"	де́лать	_____
"to speak"	говори́ть	_____
"to look at"	посмотре́ть	_____
"to be"	быть	_____

Sights to see - Достопримеча́тельности
Москва́ - Moscow

The All Russia Exhibition Centre
Arbat Street
The Bolshoy Theatre
Cathedral of Vassily the Blessed
Cathedral of Christ the Saviour
Izmailovsky Park
Kolomenskoye
The Kremlin
Lenin's Mausoleum
The Lubyanka
The Main Universal Shop
The Moscow Circus
The Moscow Metro

Moscow State University
Novodevichy Monastery
The Ostankino Tower
Park of Culture
Red Square
The Tretyakov Gallery
The Tsar cannon
The White House

Бе́лый дом
Большо́й теа́тр
ВВЦ (Всеросси́йский вы́ставочный центр)
ГУМ (Гла́вный универса́льный магази́н)
Изма́йловский парк
Коло́менское
Кра́сная пло́щадь
Кремль
Лубя́нка
Мавзоле́й Ле́нина
МГУ (Моско́вский Госуда́рственный Университе́т)
Моско́вское метро́
Моско́вский цирк
Новоде́вичий монасты́рь
Оста́нкинская ба́шня

Pair up the Russian and English names and tick off what you have seen.

Парк культу́ры
Третьяко́вская галере́я
Улица Арба́т
Храм Васи́лия Блаже́нного
Храм Христа́ Спаси́теля
Царь-пу́шка

Sights to see - Достопримеча́тельности
Санкт-Петербу́рг - Saint Petersburg

The Bronze Horseman
Cathedral of the Spilled Blood
The cruiser "Aurora"
Isaac's Cathedral
The Hermitage
The Mariinsky Theatre
The Museum of the Blockade of Leningrad
The River Neva
Nevsky Prospect
The Palace Square
The Peter and Paul Fortress

Smolny
Tsarskoye Selo
The Yusupov Palace

Дворцо́вая пло́щадь
Исаа́киевский собо́р
Кре́йсер «Авро́ра»
Мари́йнский теа́тр
Ме́дный вса́дник
Музе́й блока́ды Ленингра́да
Не́вский проспе́кт
Пе́тро-Па́вловская кре́пость
Река́ Нева́
Смо́льный
Храм Спа́са-на-Крови́
Ца́рское село́
Эрмита́ж
Юсу́повский дворе́ц

Pair up the Russian and English names and tick off what you have seen.

Moscow metro stations

Find the station signs and work out how they
are pronounced.

Airport (This is a former military airfield, not an airport!)
Dinamo
Komsomolskaya
Lubyanka
Park of Culture
Revolution Square

_____   _____

_____   _____   _____   _____

_____

Signs and other useful words

Some of these words may also be in the a to я section of this book.

Автóбус	_____	Bus
Áдрес	_____	Adress
Аптéка	_____	Chemist
Аэропóрт	_____	Airport
Банк	_____	Bank
Банкомáт	_____	Cash machine
Бар	_____	Bar
Бензи́н	_____	Petrol
Биле́т	_____	Ticket
Буфéт	_____	Snack bar
Бюрó	_____	Office
Ви́за	_____	Visa

Визи́тка	_____	Visiting card
Вокза́л	_____	Station
Вход	_____	Entry
Нет вхо́да	_____	No entry
Вы́ход	_____	Exit
Гости́ница	_____	Hotel
Душ	_____	Shower
Интерне́т	_____	Internet
За́втрак	_____	Breakfast
Закры́то	_____	Closed
За́нято	_____	Occupied
Запрещено́	_____	Forbidden
К себе́	_____	Pull ("Towards oneself")

Ка́сса	_____	Pay point
Кафе́	_____	Café
Кварти́ра	_____	Flat, apartment
Кио́ск	_____	Kiosk
Кино́	_____	Cinema
Клуб	_____	Club
Ключ	_____	Key
Купе́	_____	Compartment (in train)
Ке́мпинг	_____	Camping
Ле́стница	_____	Stairs
Лифт	_____	Lift
Магази́н	_____	Shop
Метро́	_____	Metro

Музе́й	_____	Museum
Но́мер	_____	Hotel room or number
Обе́д	_____	Lunch
Обме́н	_____	Exchange
О́пера	_____	Opera
Остано́вка	_____	Bus stop
От себя́	_____	Push ("Away from oneself")
Откры́то	_____	Open
Па́мятник	_____	Monument
Парк	_____	Park
Па́спорт	_____	Passport
Перехо́д	_____	Crossing or underpass
План	_____	Map or plan
Платфо́рма	_____	Platform

Пло́щадь	_____	Square
Поли́ция	_____	Police
По́езд	_____	Train
По́чта	_____	Post
Пробле́ма	_____	Problem
Проду́кты	_____	Food products
Про́пуск	_____	Pass (for a hotel etc.)
Путь	_____	Track (for a train etc.)
Расписа́ние	_____	Timetable
Регистра́ция	_____	Registration, Check in
Ремо́нт	_____	Repairs
Рестора́н	_____	Restaurant
Рубль	_____	Rouble
Самообслу́живание	_____	Self service

Сейф	_____	A safe
Спорт	_____	Sport
Стадио́н	_____	Stadium
Ста́нция	_____	Station (metro, bus, etc.)
Стоя́нка	_____	Parking place or taxi rank
Сувени́ры	_____	Souvenirs
Такси́	_____	Taxi
Теа́тр	_____	Theatre
Телефо́н	_____	Telephone
Термина́л	_____	Terminal
Трамва́й	_____	Tram
Транзи́т	_____	Transit
Тролле́йбус	_____	Trolleybus

Туале́т
_____ Toilet

M - men   Ж - women

У́лица _____ Street

У́жин _____ Supper

Центр _____ Centre

Экску́рсия _____ Excursion

Эта́ж _____ Floor

Menu reader
Write in the sounds

Ресторáн	_____	Restaurant
Меню́	_____	Menu
Официáнт	_____	Waiter
Официáнтка	_____	Waitress
Закýски	_____	Starters
Салáт	_____	Salad
Пирожки́	_____	Small pies
Пéрвые блю́да	_____	First dishes (usually soups)
Суп	_____	Soup

Борщ	_____	Beetroot soup
Щи	_____	Cabbage soup
Уха́	_____	A fish soup
Окро́шка	_____	Cold soup (served in summer)

Вторы́е блю́да _____ Second (main) dishes

Говя́дина	_____	Beef
Свини́на	_____	Pork
Лосо́сь	_____	Salmon
Ку́рица	_____	Chicken
Пиро́г	_____	Pie
Шашлы́к	_____	Shashlyk
Карто́шка	_____	Potato

Сла́дкое	_____	Dessert
Блины́	_____	Pancakes
Моро́женое	_____	Ice cream
Фрукто́вый сала́т	_____	Fruit salad
Напи́тки	_____	Drinks
Вино́	_____	Wine
Во́дка	_____	Vodka
Пи́во	_____	Beer
Минера́льная вода́	_____	Mineral water
Сок	_____	Juice
Чай	_____	Tea
Ко́фе	_____	Coffee

Блинная - _____

Here you can buy pancakes - блины.

What can you have with them?

Мёд	_____	Honey
Сыр	_____	Cheese
Варенье	_____	Jam

Which is which restaurant?

①

② ЦЕНТР АЗЕРБАЙДЖАНСКОЙ КУЛИНАРИИ

ресторан «БАКУ»

③ ЯПОНСКИЙ РЕСТОРАН

④ Кафе Болоньезе ИТАЛИЯ КАК ОНА ЕСТЬ М, Дмитровка, д.6 699-07-70

Azerbaijani
Brazilian
Chinese
Italian
Japanese
Sicilian

⑤

КИТАЙСКИЙ РЕСТОРАН

⑥

БРАЗИЛЬЕРО

БРАЗИЛЬСКИЙ РЕСТОРАН
-1 ЭТАЖ

Football - Футбóл

Cities where matches will be played in the 2018 World Cup:

Волгогрáд   _____

Екатеринбу́рг   _____

Казáнь   _____

Калинингрáд   _____

Москвá   _____

Ни́жний Нóвгород   _____

Ростóв на Дону́   _____

Самáра   _____

Санкт-Петербу́рг   _____

Сарáнск   _____

Сóчи   _____

Football vocabulary

Ку́бок ми́ра   _____ World Cup

Стадио́н   _____ Stadium

Кома́нда   _____ Team

Сбо́рная   _____ National team

Боле́льщик   _____ Fan

Фина́л   _____ Final

Полуфина́л   _____ Semi Final

Тре́нер   _____ Trainer

Игро́к   _____ Player

Ре́фери   _____ Referee

Свисто́к   _____ Whistle

Ла́йнсмен   _____ Linesman

Fans in Samara

Пе́рвый тайм	_____	First half
Второ́й тайм	_____	Second half
Доба́вленное вре́мя		
	_____	Added time
Мяч	_____	Ball
Воро́та	_____	Goalposts
Се́тка	_____	Net
А́ут	_____	Out
Офса́йд	_____	Offside
Гол	_____	Goal
Нет го́ла	_____	No goal
Наруше́ние	_____	Foul
Пена́льти	_____	Penalty

Угловóй	_____	Corner
Рикошéт	_____	Deflection
Счёт	_____	Score
Побéда	_____	A win
Пораже́ние	_____	A defeat
Ничья́	_____	A draw
Трáвма	_____	Injury
Замéна	_____	Substitution
Жёлтая кáрточка	_____	Yellow card
Крáсная кáрточка	_____	Red card

Some Russian teams and their cities

«Локомоти́в» Москва́ _____

«Спарта́к» Москва́ _____

«Дина́мо» Москва́ _____

«Зени́т» Санкт-Петербу́рг _____

«Кры́лья Сове́тов» Сама́ра _____
  Wings of the Soviets

«Ши́нник» Яросла́вль _____
  Tyre factory

«Торпе́до» Москва́ _____

«Росто́в» Росто́в-на-Дону́ _____

«АНЖИ́» Махачкала́ _____

Some emergency phrases

Let's hope you don't have any emergencies, but here are some useful phrases just in case.
Write in the sounds of the Russian words.

Use the recordings from
www.ruslan.co.uk/alphabetstarter.htm
for the best pronunciation.

Я англича́нин. _____   I am English (male).

Я англича́нка. _____   I am English (female).

(The Russians often use англича́нин / англича́нка to mean anyone from the UK!)

Вот мой па́спорт.

_____   Here is my passport.

Моя́ гости́ница – «Ко́смос».

_____   My hotel is "Kosmos".

Где метро́? _____   Where is the metro?

Мне ну́жно такси́.

_____   I need a taxi.

У меня́ нет де́нег. _____   I have no money.

Я не понима́ю. _____ I don't understand.

Вы говори́те по-англи́йски?

_____ Do you speak English?

Мне пло́хо.

_____ I feel ill.

Мне ну́жен до́ктор.

_____ I need a doctor.

Где туале́т? _____ Where is the toilet?

Где Брита́нское посо́льство?

_____ Where is the British Embassy?

English names in Russian

Russian does not have several sounds that we have in English, such as "h", "j", "th", "w", "ng".
Here are the Russian spellings of some British names. Write in the names in English and try
the Russian pronunciation.

Бра́унинг   _____

Джо́унс   _____

Джэ́ксон   _____

Кук   _____

Макдо́нальд   _____

Прайс   _____

Смит   _____

Уэ́ст   _____

Ха́ррис   _____

What is the name of the pub?

Key to the exercises

Page 19   1. Museum, 2. Wine, 3. Supermarket, 4. Cash machine, 5. Toilet, 6. Stop, 7. Café,
           8. Photos.
Page 20   1. Novosibirsk, 2. Saint Petersburg, 3. Moscow.
Page 86   1. Sicilian, 2. Azerbaijani, 3. Japanese, 4. Italian, 5. Chinese, 6. Brazilian.
Page 94   Browning, Jones, Jackson, Cook, MacDonald, Price, Smith, West, Harris.
           The John Bull Pub.

Notes:

The Ruslan Russian Course by John Langran and Natalya Veshnyeva

This is a three stage communicative Russian course from beginners to advanced level, based on up to date, realistic dialogues and with clear grammatical explanations, exercises, language games for the classroom, and lots of fun. Follow the story of Ivan, Lyudmila, Zoya Petrovna, Vadim and Peter, and of the typical foreigner!

The first lesson is free at www.ruslan.co.uk/demos.htm

Ruslan 1 fifth edition textbook   ISBN 9781899785827
Ruslan 1 fifth edition textbook with audio CD   ISBN 9781899785834
Ruslan 1 workbook with audio CD   ISBN 9781899785223
Ruslan 1 Lessons 1-5 cartoons   ISBN 9781899785926
For Ruslan 2 and 3 and for other Ruslan publications go to www.ruslan.co.uk

The Ruslan Russian course has been published in the USA, Italy, the Netherlands and China, and there are versions for French, German and Swedish-speaking learners.